Kitchen Sugar Lab

Jen Malone
& Paul Beck

becker&mayer! kids

Brimming with creative inspiration, how-to projects, and useful
information to enrich your everyday life, Quarto Knows is a favorite
destination for those pursuing their interests and passions. Visit our
site and dig deeper with our books into your area of interest:
Quarto Creates, Quarto Cooks, Quarto Homes, Quarto Lives,
Quarto Drives, Quarto Explores, Quarto Gifts, or Quarto Kids.

Published in 2021 by becker&mayer! kids, an imprint of The Quarto Group,
11120 NE 33rd Place, Suite 201, Bellevue, WA 98004 USA.
www.QuartoKnows.com

This book is part of the *Kitchen Sugar Science* kit and is not to be sold separately.

becker&mayer! kids titles are also available at discount for retail, wholesale, promotional, and bulk purchase. For details,
contact the Special Sales Manager by email at specialsales@quarto.com or by mail at The Quarto Group, Attn: Special
Sales Manager, 100 Cummings Center Suite 265D, Beverly, MA 01915 USA.

21 22 23 24 25   5 4 3 2 1

ISBN: 978-0-7603-7232-6

Digital edition published in 2021
eISBN: 978-0-7603-7233-3

Library of Congress Cataloging-in-Publication Data available upon request.

Authors: Jen Malone and Paul Beck
Illustration: Oliver Crowell

Printed, manufactured, and assembled in Shenzhen, China, 07/21

Distributed by:
Quarto UK, The Old Brewery
6 Blundell Street, London N7 9BH, UK
Allen & Unwin
30 Centre Rd, Scoresby VIC 3179, AUS

Image credits: photos from Shutterstock
Disclaimer text: Complies with CPSIA

#345386

Table of Contents

Your Kit

Sugar and spice and everything nice—that's what this book has in store for you. Even better than the fun you'll have conducting these experiments is the sweet taste of victory you'll experience while eating your finished creations.

BEFORE YOU BEGIN:

- Scrub-a-dub the gummy mold in warm, soapy water.

- Gather the listed ingredients and read through the instructions before beginning each experiment. Some require adult assistance and others will take more than one day to complete, so it is best to know what you're getting yourself into beforehand.

*Caution: CHOKING HAZARD - Children under 8 yrs can choke or suffocate on uninflated or broken balloons. Adult supervision required. Keep uninflated balloons from Children. Discard broken balloons at once.

Your Kit Includes:

Gummy Mold

2 Rubber Latex Balloons

Bubble Wand

5 Rock Candy Sticks

Pretty Please with Sugar on Top:
READ THESE SAFETY GUIDELINES!

Several experiments in this kit require the use of a stovetop. You should have an adult help with these. Heated sugar can cause burns if it comes in contact with your skin. Always use caution when performing an experiment.

INGREDIENTS:

Not every experiment requires this full list of ingredients, but to complete all the offerings in this book, you will need:

- [ ] White sugar (of course!)
- [ ] Active dry yeast
- [ ] Flavored gelatin (such as Jell-O)
- [ ] Unflavored gelatin
- [ ] Flavoring extracts
- [ ] Food coloring
- [ ] Powdered lemonade mix with citric acid (such as Crystal Lite)
- [ ] Full-sized marshmallows
- [ ] An assortment of candies and/or sprinkles
- [ ] Wintergreen mint candies
- [ ] Vegetable oil or cooking spray
- [ ] Fruit juice (any type)
- [ ] Dish soap (NOT antibacterial)
- [ ] Light brown sugar
- [ ] Vanilla extract
- [ ] Light oil (such as olive, sunflower, or coconut)

TOOLS:

- [ ] Regular pliers (not needle-nosed)
- [ ] Plastic bag that zips closed
- [ ] Measuring cup
- [ ] Measuring spoons
- [ ] Empty water bottle
- [ ] Saucepan
- [ ] Stovetop
- [ ] Wooden stirring spoon
- [ ] Small mixing bowl
- [ ] Popsicle stick or butter knife
- [ ] Parchment paper
- [ ] Five glass jars
- [ ] Five clothespins
- [ ] Ladle

What Is Sugar?

Carbohydrates are a type of energy your body runs on, like gasoline is a type of energy that cars run on. Sugar is the smallest and simplest of all carbohydrates.

You might have been refused a sugary treat because it will leave you "bouncing off the walls." That burst of energy is sometimes called a sugar rush, and it happens because your body converts sugar really quickly into get-up-and-go (and go, and go, and go) energy! But because your body burns the energy made from sugar just as easily as it makes it, a "sugar crash" follows.

Cars of the future may run on sugar. Sugar is the main ingredient of rocket candy—a fuel used to make model rockets shoot into the air. Scientists are currently working on ways to make a similar fuel that could power our cars.

Sweetness is the only taste we're born craving!

Why is Sugar So Delicious?

Blame the cavepeople for your sweet tooth. In prehistoric times, people couldn't be sure when their next meal was coming. Eating sugary treats like fruits and berries helped these early humans add fat to their bodies that could be converted to energy during times when food was scarce. Having enough energy to do things like escape saber-toothed tigers was essential to survival, so humans learned to seek out sugary foods.

Sweet Facts

Sugar naturally occurs in fruits, dairy, grains, and vegetables. Plus, a process known as photosynthesis creates sugar in the fibers of all plants. Imagine grass as an ice cream topping!

Humans might be born craving sugar, but not cats. Felines do not have sweetness receptors in their brains. Neither do dolphins or sea lions. But dogs experience sugar like you and would be more than happy to share that vanilla pudding.

A scientist was trying to create a chemical to repel bugs. When he accidentally tasted his experiment, he noticed that it tasted sweet. That's how he discovered sucralose, which you might know as Splenda. That's a sweet accident!

More than half of the 8.4 million metric tons of sugar produced annually in the United States comes from beets. Next time someone nags you to eat your vegetables, you can whip out this sweet fact!

Mary Poppins says a spoonful of sugar helps the medicine go down, but once upon a time, sugar was the medicine. As far back as the ninth century, Middle Eastern people were using sugars in medicinal syrups and powders. Just a few centuries ago, sugar was prescribed by doctors to cure all kinds of diseases.

Back in the 12th century, when sugar first reached the shores of England, it was called a spice and used by the very, very rich to flavor their food.

Far out! A form of sugar called glycolaldehyde has been found in clouds of gas and dust near the center of the Milky Way and on the surface of the comet Lovejoy.

A man in Germany currently owns the Guinness World Record for the largest collection of sugar packets. At the time his record was certified, he had 14,502 different packets.

1

Sugar Sparks

WHAT YOU'LL NEED:

- Wintergreen mint candies
- Regular pliers (not needle-nosed)
- Plastic bag that zips closed
- Completely dark room. Closets work great!

Razzle dazzle with a crackling light display!

WHAT TO DO:

1 First, practice steps 2-4 in the light, so your hands will know what to do in the dark.

2 Seal a few mints inside the plastic bag.

3 Position the pliers on the outside of the bag around a mint inside the bag.

4 Squeeze pliers to crush the candy. Be careful of your fingers!

5 Refill the empty bag with new mints before moving into the dark room.

6 Allow your eyes at least five minutes to adjust to the dark. This might be boring, but the longer you wait, the brighter the candy spark will appear.

7 Repeat steps 2-4 in the dark. Crush all the mints and marvel at the faint glows that appear with each squeeze of your pliers!

How'd I Do That?

Ever accidentally touch a metal doorknob after shuffling your feet across a carpet? OUCH! You experienced static electricity. When a material is pushed, pulled, scratched, crushed, or rubbed, the electrical charges inside it separate and move around. Under the right conditions, all that moving electricity causes tiny sparks.

2 Burping Balloons

WHAT YOU'LL NEED:

- Measuring cup
- Measuring spoons
- ¼ cup (60mL) warm (but not hot!) water
- 1 teaspoon (5mL) active dry yeast
- 1 teaspoon (5mL) sugar
- An uninflated balloon*
- An empty water bottle

Blame the burp on the balloon! Create a belch with sugar and yeast.

WHAT TO DO:

1 Blow up the balloon then let all the air out. Repeat at least twice to really *strrrrrreeeeettttttttttch* out that balloon.

2 Measure your ingredients.

3 Pour both the warm water and the dry yeast into the water bottle and gently swirl the bottle until all the yeast has dissolved.

4 Now add the sugar and swirl until dissolved.

5 Fit the opening of the balloon over the opening of the water bottle.

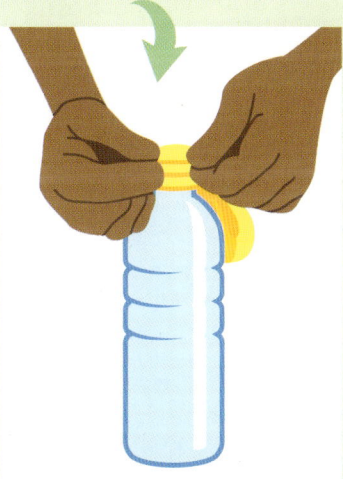

6 When you check back a few hours later, the balloon will have inflated.

How'd I Do That?

It's alive! The yeast, that is. Yeast is actually a tiny, living organism, and when living things eat, they take in air. The air consists of gases, which need to escape. When yeast eats sugar and air, it needs to burp out carbon dioxide gas, which inflates the balloon. Better out than in!

Carbon Dioxide ➤

Yeast

3

Sugar Snowman

WHAT YOU'LL NEED:

- Measuring cup
- ¼ cup (60mL) hot water
- ¼ cup (60mL) sugar
- Marshmallows
- Small candies or sprinkles for decorating your snowman
- Saucepan
- Stovetop
- Spoon for stirring
- Small mixing bowl
- Popsicle stick or butter knife for spreading "glue"
- An adult to help

Sweet as a...snowman? Build your own sugar creature!

WHAT TO DO:

1 Pour the hot water and sugar into the mixing bowl and stir briskly to dissolve most of the sugar.

2 Place the saucepan onto the stovetop and pour the contents of the mixing bowl into it. Ask your adult helper to set the heat to medium high and stir occasionally until the mixture begins to boil.

3 Once the syrup begins to boil, reduce the heat to low and let it simmer for five minutes.

4 Carefully pour the syrup back into the mixing bowl and leave it to cool. Once it is cool, move to step 5.

5 Using your popsicle stick or butter knife, spread the syrup on the tops of the marshmallows, then "glue" them together.

6 Use the "glue" to attach additional candy, such as eyes, nose, or maybe even a hat.

How'd I Do That?

If your ice cream has ever dripped on you, you know the truth: wet sugar is STICKY! But why?

Sugar

Water

Think about a Velcro tab on a shoe. When the Velcro is unfastened, neither side is very sticky. But when you match the two strips up, they hold onto each other.

Your sugar is one side of a strip of Velcro. Water represents the other strip of Velcro. When the water and the sugar meet up, a bunch of the molecules in the sugar jump over to match up with the molecules in the water. Just like two pieces of Velcro coming together.

4 Rock Candy

WHAT YOU'LL NEED:

- ½ cup (120mL) hot water, plus ¼ cup (60 mL) for stick preparation
- 1¼ cup (300mL) sugar, plus ¼ cup (60 mL) and additional 1 tablespoon for the sticks
- Wooden lollipop sticks
- Parchment paper
- Mixing bowl
- Measuring cups
- Tablespoon
- Glass jars (one per lollipop stick)
- Clothespins (one per lollipop stick)
- Saucepan
- Stovetop
- Wooden stirring spoon
- Food coloring
- Adult to assist

What's better than a cool crystal science experiment? One you can eat, of course!

WHAT TO DO:

DAY 1

1 Combine ¼ cup water and ¼ cup sugar in the bowl, then stir to dissolve the sugar.

2 Pour an additional spoonful of sugar into a small pile on the parchment paper.

3 Dunk ¾ of a lollipop stick into the sugar water to wet it. Leave enough room to hold the stick with your hand.

4 Roll the sugar water end of the lollipop stick in the pile of sugar to coat it with sugar crystals.

5 Place carefully on parchment paper to dry overnight.

DAY 2

1 Combine 1¼ cup sugar and ½ cup hot water in a mixing bowl, stirring to dissolve.

2 Pour the mixture into the saucepan, then have your adult assistant help you heat it over medium-low heat until the mixture comes to a boil, stirring occasionally. Try to keep sugar crystals away from the sides of the saucepan.

3 Once the mixture has begun to boil, continue stirring until all of the sugar has dissolved and the liquid is clear. If you want colorful rock candy, now add several drops of food coloring.

4 Find a spot to place your glass jars where they won't be bumped or disturbed for several days.

5 Have your adult assistant pour or ladle the contents of the saucepan into the jars, dividing it evenly among them. The solution should fill the jar enough to cover the part of the stick you coated in sugar.

6 Lightly tap your lollipop sticks over a sink or trashcan to remove any loose sugar crystals, then use a clothespin to suspend the lollipop in the glass jar.

7 Check back in a couple days to see the crystals slowly beginning to form on the lollipop stick. When you're satisfied with the amount of rock candy on your stick, remove the stick and enjoy!

How'd I Do That?

Sugar grains are tiny crystals, and crystals like to form on top of each other. When you coated the lollipop stick in sugar water and rolled it in dry sugar, you "glued" the first layer of sugar crystals to the stick, which invited other sugar crystals to join that layer. There weren't any other sugar crystals around... until you suspended the lollipop stick over a jar full of dissolved sugar, that is. As the water in the jar evaporated a little bit each hour, the crystallized sugar molecules left behind joined the original sugar layer.

5 Wiggle Worms

WHAT YOU'LL NEED:

- ¼ cup (60 mL) cold water
- 2 tablespoons (30 mL) corn syrup
- 3 tablespoons (45 mL) flavored gelatin
- 1 3-oz (85 g) packet unflavored gelatin
- Gummy mold
- Measuring cups and spoons
- Mixing bowl
- Saucepan
- Stirring spoon
- Ladle (optional)
- Stovetop
- Adult to assist

Create your own candy, and let it worm its way into your mouth!

WHAT TO DO:

1 Pour cold water and corn syrup into the mixing bowl and stir until the liquid is clear.

2 Add the flavored gelatin and the package of unflavored gelatin to the bowl and gently stir until the powders have dissolved.

3 Pour the mixture into the saucepan and ask your adult assistant to help heat it on medium low heat until the mixture begins to bubble (approximately ten minutes), stirring throughout.

4 Remove the pan from the heat.

5 Carefully pour or ladle the gelatin into the worm molds.

6 Allow the mixture to set in the mold for one hour.

7 It's YUM time! Enjoy those squiggly worms!

How'd I Do That?

One of the ingredients in your worms is gelatin. Gelatin has pockets. If you look at gelatin under a microscope, you see little spaces of air between the sugar molecules. Those pockets trap liquid. Corn syrup is a liquid form of sugar, so when you mixed it with gelatin, the syrup filled those empty spaces. As the mixture cooled off, the molecules gelled together into a squishy consistency.

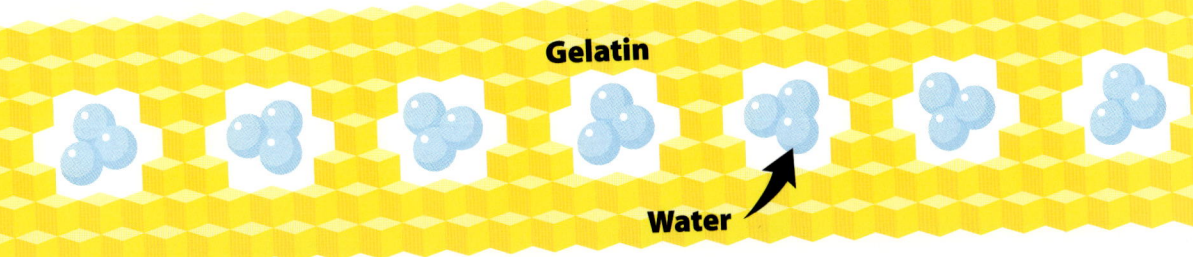

Gelatin

Water

Those pockets still have a small bit of space left in them, which is why submersing your gummy worm in water overnight will cause it to grow!

Experiment

6 Sour Worms

WHAT YOU'LL NEED:

- ¼ cup (60 mL) cold water
- 2 tablespoons (30 mL) corn syrup
- 3 tablespoons (45 mL) flavored gelatin
- 1 3-oz (85 g) packet unflavored gelatin
- Gummy mold
- 2 tablespoons of flavored lemonade powdered mix (make sure it contains citric acid)
- Measuring cups and spoons
- Mixing bowl
- Saucepan
- Stirring spoon
- Ladle (optional)
- Stovetop
- Adult to assist

Sometimes sticky sweet is a tad too much—use sour to balance it out!

WHAT TO DO:

1 Pour cold water and corn syrup into the mixing bowl and stir until the liquid is clear.

2 Add the flavored gelatin and the package of unflavored gelatin to the bowl and gently stir until the powders have dissolved.

3 Pour the mixture into the saucepan and ask your adult assistant to help heat it on medium low heat until the mixture begins to bubble (approximately ten minutes), stirring throughout.

4 Remove the pan from heat.

5 Carefully pour or ladle the gelatin into the worm molds.

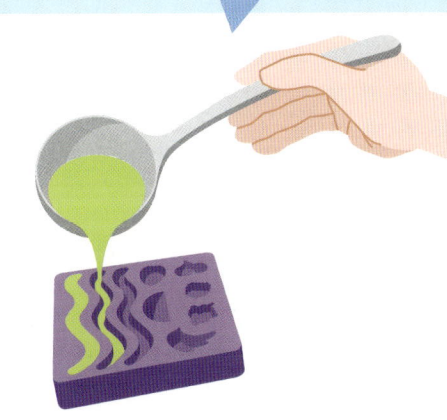

6 Allow the mixture to set in the mold for one hour.

7 Pour the powdered lemonade onto a countertop or piece of parchment paper.

8 Carefully remove gummy worms from the mold and roll each in the powdered lemonade to coat.

How'd I Do That?

Did you know lemons have more sugar than strawberries? It's true! But lemons also contain citric acid, which gives lemons their sour taste. By adding sugar to your gummy worms (in the form of corn syrup), you re-balanced the flavors so you could taste both the sweet and the sour at the same time.

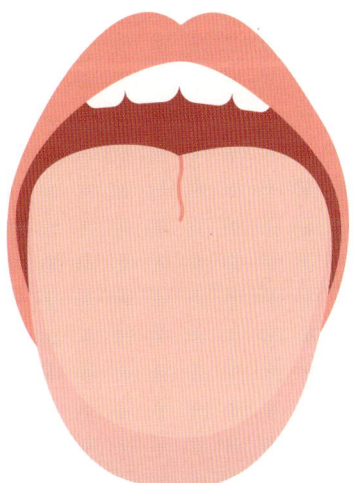

There are five basic tastes humans can experience on our tongues: sweet, salty, sour, bitter, and umami.

7

Trickster Gummies

WHAT YOU'LL NEED:

- Vegetable oil or cooking spray
- 1 3-oz (25 g) packet of unflavored gelatin
- 3 tablespoons plus 1 tablespoon (45 mL plus 15 mL) fruit juice (any variety)
- 1 tablespoon (15 mL) sugar
- ½ teaspoon (2.5 mL) honey
- Flavoring extracts (any variety, several drops each)
- Food coloring (several drops each)
- Gummy mold
- Measuring spoons
- Mixing bowl
- Saucepan
- Stirring spoon
- Ladle (optional)
- Stovetop
- Adult to assist

It's fun to be sweet AND sassy—so fool your friends with these oddball flavors!

WHAT TO DO:

1 Lightly coat the gummy worm mold with cooking spray or vegetable oil.

2 Pour the gelatin packet and 3 tablespoons juice into the unheated saucepan and allow to sit, unstirred, for 15 minutes.

3 While you wait, combine 1 tablespoon sugar and 1 tablespoon juice in your mixing bowl and stir until sugar dissolves.

4 Return to the saucepan and ask an adult to help heat the gelatin mixture over medium heat until the powder dissolves into the liquid. Stir occasionally.

5 Remove the saucepan from the heat.

6 Pour the contents of the mixing bowl into the saucepan, along with a ½ teaspoon honey, a couple drops of food coloring, and a couple drops of flavoring. Get creative with your color and flavor combos here: the weirder, the trickier! Stir until well mixed.

7 Spoon or ladle the mixture into the gummy molds.

8 Allow the molds to harden.

9 Gross out your favorite people with the unexpected flavors!

How'd I Do That?

You taste with your tongue, but you also taste with your nose and your eyes and even your brain. When you see a purple candy, your brain says you're about to eat something grape-flavored based on your past experiences. When it turns out to be strawberry-flavored, it takes a few seconds for your brain to register the unexpected taste. What strange combos can you come up with?

8

Not-So-Gummy Sugar Worms

WHAT YOU'LL NEED:

- 1 cup (240 mL) sugar
- 1 teaspoon (5 mL) water
- Gummy mold
- Measuring spoons
- Mixing bowl

A worm that melts on your tongue!

WHAT TO DO:

1 Combine 1 teaspoon water and 1 cup sugar in a mixing bowl, then stir energetically until the mixture looks and feels like damp sand.

2 Spoon the mixture into the gummy mold, stopping when it is halfway full to tightly press the sugar into the mold before filling it the rest of the way.

3 Tightly press again, making sure the mold is packed as tightly as you can get it.

4 Leave the mold in the open air overnight to dry.

5 Slowly and gently, push up on the bottom of the mold to release your sugar worms. Use them wherever you would use a sugar cube!

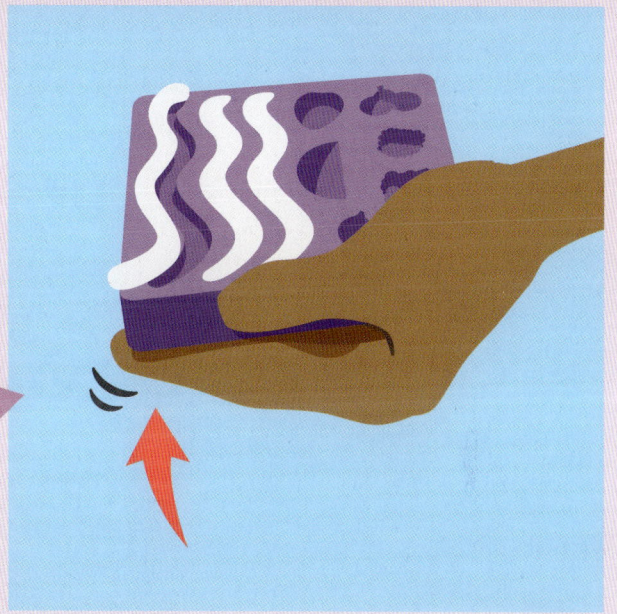

How'd I Do That?

If you've ever made a sandcastle, you know the best sand is not too wet but not too dry. There, the water acts like a glue holding the sand grains together. Damp sand holds its shape when released, even after the water inside begins to evaporate.

Sugar cubes do the same thing. When you press the damp mixture tightly into the gummy mold, the water melts the sugar crystals together. But too much water causes destruction. Just like a wave crashing over a sandcastle leaves a melted, mushy mess, sugar cubes (or sugar worms!) completely dissolve when placed in a glass of liquid.

Experiment 9

Sugar Bubbles

WHAT YOU'LL NEED:

- ¾ cup (180 mL) hot water
- 1 tablespoon (15 mL) sugar
- 2 tablespoon (30 mL) dish soap (avoid antibacterial and/or ultra concentrated)
- Mixing bowl
- Measuring cup and spoons
- Stirring spoon
- Bubble blowing tools such as the included bubble wand, a drinking straw, or a plastic funnel.

A spoonful of sugar helps the bubble last longer!

WHAT TO DO:

1 In the mixing bowl, combine water and sugar, stirring until the sugar dissolves.

2 Very slowly add dish soap, stirring GENTLY. Try not to create suds.

3 Once mixed, you have your bubble solution. Dip your bubble wand in and start blowing bubbles!

Want More Bubble Fun?
Try Making a Bubble Inside A Bubble

WHAT YOU'LL NEED:

- Sugar bubble solution
- Shallow pan
- Small bowl
- Plastic drinking straw (the thinner, the better; a coffee stirring straw works great)

WHAT TO DO:

1 Pour about ¼ cup (60 mL) of sugar bubble solution into the bowl and the rest into the shallow pan.

2 Dip the drinking straw into the bowl, then remove it and poke it into the center of the pan.

3 Blow very gently into the straw. This should create a large, dome-shaped bubble in your pan.

4 Pull the straw carefully from the bubble, then poke it back in and blow a second bubble inside the first.

⚠ CHALLENGE:
See if you can blow a THIRD bubble inside the second one!

10 *Sugar Scrub*

WHAT YOU'LL NEED:

- 1 tablespoon (15 mL) white sugar
- 1 tablespoon (15 mL) light brown sugar
- 1 teaspoon (5 mL) of any light oil, such as olive, sunflower, or coconut
- Measuring spoons
- Mixing bowl
- Stirring spoon
- Optional: 2 drops vanilla extract or other essential oil for fragrance

Sugar can be a treat for your skin, as well as your tongue!

WHAT TO DO:

1 Combine all ingredients into the mixing bowl and stir well.

2 Wet your hands.

3 Scoop some mixture into your hands and rub it in thoroughly, coating both sides of each hand.

4 Rinse your hands and enjoy your smooth skin.

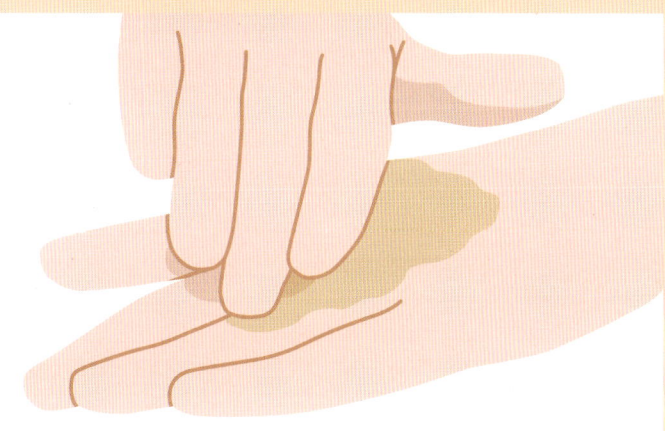

How'd I Do That?

People use sandpaper to smooth out pieces of wood. Sugar crystals act like a gentle sandpaper for your skin, brushing off the layer of dead skin cells and exposing the newer, smoother skin underneath. The sugar scrub also keeps your skin hydrated by attracting moisture.

Sugar Crystal   **Dead Skin Cell**

While a sugar scrub speeds up the process, you lose old skin cells without its help. In fact, you lose between 30,000 and 40,000 every minute! That's almost nine pounds of skin a year!

Glossary

Atom:
A single building block for every substance on Earth. When two or more atoms join together, they form a molecule.

Bitter:
One of the five tastes the human tongue can detect. An example of a bitter food is unsweetened cranberries.

Carbohydrate:
Sugars (like candy) or starches (like rice or potatoes) that your body converts into energy to feed your cells.

Carbon Dioxide:
A colorless, odorless gas that you release into the air when you exhale.

Evaporation:
When liquid (such as water) is turned into a gas.

Fats:
Like carbohydrates, fats are another nutrient your body converts into energy.

Immune System:
A network of cells, organs, and tissues in our body that works together to protect us from diseases and fight off sickness.

Molecules:

When two or more atoms join together, they form a molecule. All substances are made of molecules linking together in different ways.

Photosynthesis:

The process used by plants to capture sunlight and convert it into the sugars that feed it.

Protein:

A nutrient that helps your cells rebuild and grow.

Salty:

One of the five tastes the human tongue can detect. It describes foods or drinks that contain or taste of salt. An example of a salty food is potato chips.

Sour:

One of the five tastes the human tongue can detect, described as having an acidic or acid-like flavor. An example of a sour drink is lemon juice.

Static Electricity:

An electrical charge on the surface of an object that builds up in one place.

Sweet:

One of the five tastes the human tongue can detect. It is described as having the taste of sugar or honey. An example of a sweet food is a strawberry.

Umami:

One of the five tastes the human tongue can detect, described as having a savory, meaty flavor. An example of an umami food is tuna.

About the Authors

Born with a wicked sweet tooth, **Jen Malone's** favorite sweet treats are Milk Duds and cinnamon bears—though never at the same time. Jen is the author of over a dozen books for kids and teens, both fiction and non-fiction, and loves to spend any free time playing in her backyard art studio.

You can learn more about Jen and her books at **www.jenmalonewrites.com**

Paul Beck has been writing about science since 1994. His science specialties include sound, music, language, and animals. When his 20-year stint developing exhibits for Seattle's hands-on Pacific Science Center ended, he devoted himself to the life of the freelance writer. He is the author of more than 30 books for children and adults. Paul lives in Seattle, WA.